DAVID AND THE GIANT

Library of Congress catalog card number: 60-11196

DAVID AND
THE GIANT

by MIKE McCLINTOCK

Pictures by FRITZ SIEBEL

An I CAN READ Book

HARPER & ROW, PUBLISHERS
NEW YORK, EVANSTON, AND LONDON

DAVID AND
THE GIANT

David, David,

Watch your sheep.

Watch them well

And do not sleep.

High on a hill above the farm,

Watch your sheep.

Keep them from harm.

David, look in the woods back there.

You may see a lion.

You may see a bear.

David, take care!

But, David, you know what to do
If an animal comes
For the sheep—or you.
You have some stones.
You have your sling.
And you can hit almost anything.

David, take your sling and see

What you can hit.

What will it be?

That ugly bird up in the tree?

He wants a baby sheep, you know.

So hit him, David!

Make him go!

David, David, take your sling.

Put in a stone.

Give it a swing.

Swing it hard.

Now let it fly.

Let the stone go far and high.

You hit him, David!

What a blow!

You hit him hard.

Watch him go!

David, David, look around.

See that snake down on the ground!

It could kill the sheep, you know.

Swing your sling, and make it go.

Why, you can hit almost anything—

A snake on the ground, a bird on the wing.

So, David, you know what to do,

If an animal comes for the sheep—or you.

David, see that little sheep fall!

Hear him cry!

Hear him call!

Pick him up and hold him tight.

The little sheep will be all right.

Sit down near the little sheep.

Take up your harp.

Sing him to sleep.

Your song is sweet.

The sheep come near.

And even birds stop by to hear.

For you began long, long ago

To play your harp.

Sing sweet and low,

So birds and beasts and men all know

How well you sing

Almost anything.

Your father comes up from the farm.

He says, "You keep the sheep from harm.

My son, you do it very well.

But now hear what I have to tell.

Now you must go and see the King.

David, he wants to hear you sing.

"He knows your songs can make men glad.

And the King is sad,

King Saul is sad.

So go and sing

For Saul, the King."

David, here is the great King Saul.

The King just sits and looks at the wall.

He does not laugh. He does not walk.

He does not eat, or sleep, or talk.

David, play on your harp and sing.

Sing sweet and low for Saul, the King.

Sing of the stars in the dark night sky.

Sing of the light when the sun is high.

Sing of the flowers, the wind in the trees,

Sing of the moon—yes, sing of all these.

Sing and play day after day.

Your songs may send Saul's cares away.

The King feels better!

See him stand!

See him smile and take your hand.

He says, "At last I am not sad.

David, your songs have made me glad.

Your songs have sent my cares away.

Please come and sing some other day.

Now, go to the hill above the farm,

And watch your sheep.

Keep them from harm."

What is this that comes

From the woods back there?

David, David, it is a bear!

The bear is going after the sheep,

The little ones that are fast asleep.

Hurry, David, take your sling.

Put in a stone. Give it a swing.

Swing the stone!

Let it fly!

You hit the bear right in the eye!

The big bear howls and runs away.

The bear will get no sheep today.

Your father sees the big bear run.

"David," he says, "well done! Well done!

You keep the sheep from harm so well.

Now hear the news I have to tell.

"An army has come to fight King Saul.

They have a giant ten feet tall!

Goliath is the giant's name.

He fills all men with fear and shame.

King Saul wants men to help him fight.

Your brothers went to him last night.

Yes, they have gone to help King Saul.

And they will fight to save us all.

But I must stay and watch the farm.

And you must keep the sheep from harm."

The days go by as they did before.

You think of your brothers off at war.

You wish you could be

With the army of Saul.

You think of the giant ten feet tall.

And then one day—

Look! What is that?

A lion comes, a great big cat.

It keeps down low,

Silent! Slow!

David, take your sling and go!

But, David, take care!

The lion is big, as big as the bear.

You let one stone fly fast—then two.

You hit him!

Now what will he do?

He does not run!

He comes for you!

Swing hard again!

The lion is fast.

Now let the stone fly out at last.

You hit the lion on the head!

Down he goes!

The lion is dead!

Your father says, "Well done! Well done!

I saw you kill the lion, my son!

David, David, with your sling

You can kill almost anything!

"But now hear what I have to say.

I want you to go far, far away.

Take your harp and take your sling.

Go and find the camp of the King.

Take this food to your brothers there.

The trip is long. David, take care."

David, you walk and walk and walk.

No time to stop.

No time to talk.

At last, near dark, you reach a hill.

And there you stop, stand very still.

You see below in the sun's last light

The army of Saul,

And the army they fight.

When morning comes, you go on down.

You pass some farms, a little town.

At last you reach the camp of the King.

Your brothers take the food you bring.

And then they have sad news to tell.

They say the war does not go well.

The King himself is full of fear,

And so are all the others here.

David, David, hear that sound!

It shakes the trees!

It shakes the ground!

Here comes the giant ten feet tall.

Goliath comes! Hear him call!

Goliath calls, "Send out one man,

And let him fight me if he can.

If he kills me, you win the war.

If I kill him, you fight no more."

The men of Saul all shake with fright.

And not one man goes out to fight!

The giant laughs.

You hear him call,

"Is there no brave man to fight for Saul?

But no one goes.

So then you say,

"I will fight the giant today!"

Your brothers cry,

"You can not go!

Why, he could kill you with one blow!

David, you are just a boy.

He could break you like a toy."

But David, David, you just say,

"I will fight the giant today!"

Your brothers take you to King Saul.

You talk to him. You tell them all

You want to fight the giant *now*.

How will you fight him? Tell them how.

David, tell them. Let them hear.

Tell them that you had no fear

Of the jaw of the lion,

The paw of the bear,

And you have no fear

Of the giant out there.

"David, you are brave!" says Saul.

"But he is big and you are small.

He is a giant, a man of war.

And you have never fought before.

But still—I see you have no fear.

So take my armor, take my spear.

They will help you in your fight.

So go—and fight with all your might."

But David needs no spear of Saul.

You do not need such things at all.

David, you know what to do

When the giant comes for you.

David, now you go alone.

And on the way, pick up a stone.

Fit the stone inside your sling.

And as you walk,

Sing, David, sing!

The giant sees you coming out.

He calls, "Now, what is this about?

They have no men, so they send you!

Ha! I will cut you right in two!"

And now the giant takes his spear.

But, David, David, never fear!

Run, David, run up near.

You have your sling.

Swing! Swing!

Now let it fly.

Let the stone go far and high.

Swing it hard! Swing it fast!

Let the stone fly out at last.

You hit the giant on the head!

Down he goes!

The giant is dead!

David, David, the giant is dead!

The giant's men all shake with fright.

They run away. They will not fight.

The men of Saul then run out fast,

And chase them from the land at last.

David, you have won the war!

In days to come, you will win more.

And sweet will be the songs you sing.

And some day—

David will be KING!